Usborne
Wipe-Clean
Words to Copy

Use the wipe-clean pen to draw
over the dotted lines and then help
the monsters copy the words.

pen **pen**

word **word**

copy **c**

Illustrated by
Kimberley Scott

Designed by Matt Durber and Yasmin Faulkner
Words by Jessica Greenwell

At the beach

sun s___

sea s___

mat m___

bag b___

sky hut h___

s___

sip

s___

jog j___

In the night-time

owl o___

fox f___

dog d___

log l___

bat

b ___

bug

b ___

cat

c ___

web

w ___

Monster food

eat

e ___

p ie

p __

mug

m ___

pan

p ___

jar

j_ _

pot

p_ _

mix

m_ _

egg

e_ _ _

Sports day

race

flag

f _ _ _ _

jump

skip   s _ _ _

r _____

bike   b _____

j _____

gold   g _____

Monster bodies

eyes

e____

nose

n____

ear

e___

toes

t____

arm

a ___ ___

hand

h ___ ___ ___

foot

f ___ ___ ___

leg

l ___ ___

Playtime

ball b___

drum d_____

kite k___

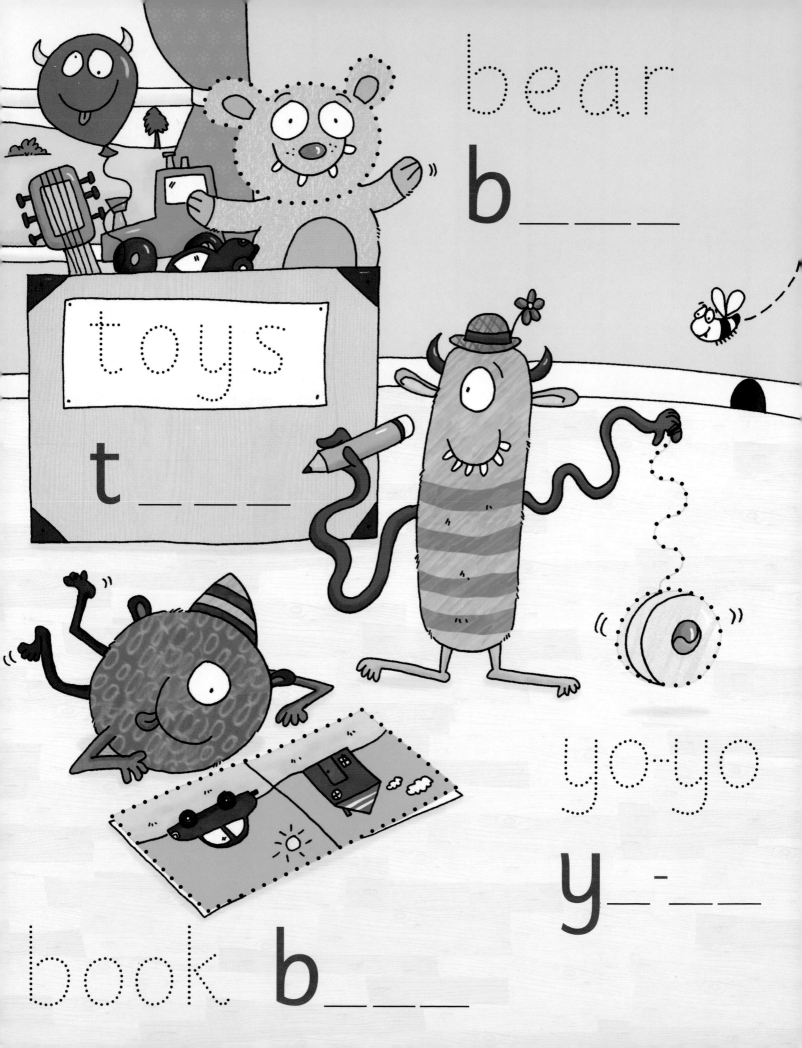

bear

b _ _ _ _

toys

t _ _ _ _

book

b _ _ _ _

yo-yo

y _ - _ _

Colours

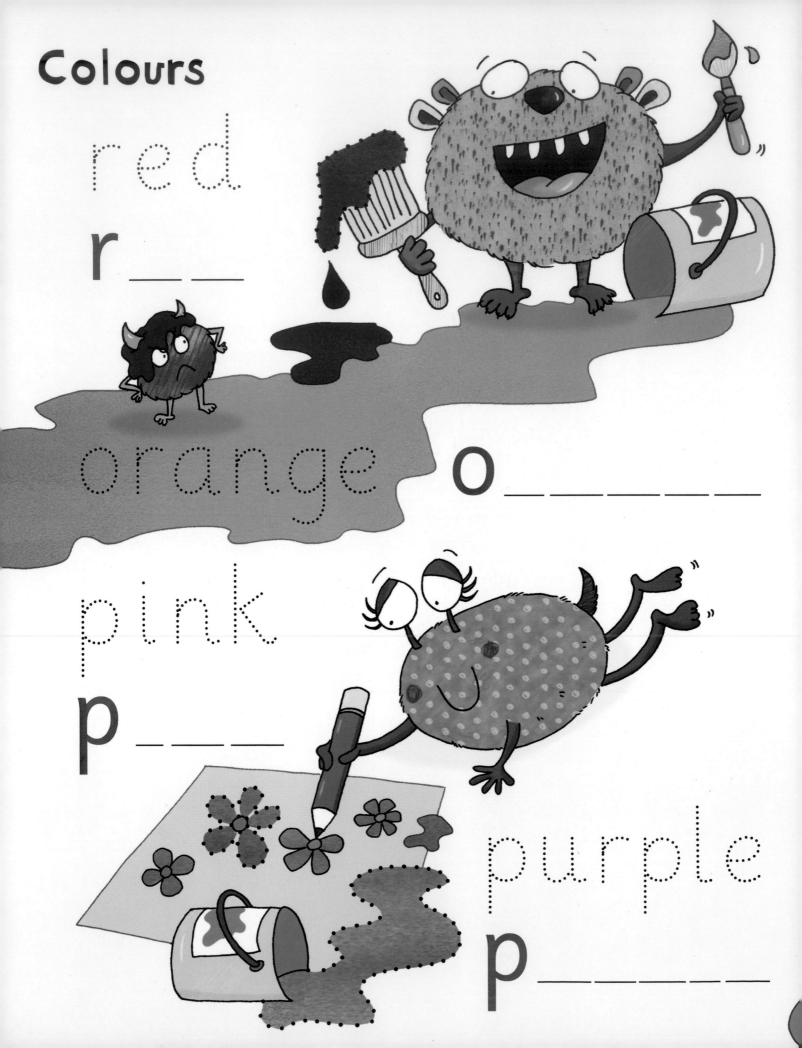

red

r _ _ _

orange

o _ _ _ _ _ _

pink

p _ _ _ _

purple

p _ _ _ _ _ _

Shapes

oval

o_____

circle

c_____

star   s____

rectangle   r_____

triangle

t_____

square

s_____

Numbers

1   one   **o**___

2   two   **t**___

3   three   **t**_____

4   four   **f**____

5   five   **f**___

6   six   **s**__

7   seven   **s**_____

8   eight   **e**_____

9   nine   **n**___

10   ten   **t**__

Days of the week

Monday   Tuesday

M_____   T_____

Wednesday

W_____

Thursday   Friday

T_____   F_____

Saturday

S_____

Sunday

S_____

Munchy's party

Finish Munchy's party invitation.
Use the words at the bottom to help you.

6

Munchy is s___.

Please come to my

party on S_____.

There will be c____

and games to p___.

It will be lots of f__.

Love Munchy

x

| six | Saturday | cake | play | fun |